Maths Challenge

Graded problems for 10–13 year-olds

Anne Joshua

STANLEY
THORNES

Copyright © Longman Cheshire 1991

First published in 1991 by
Longman Cheshire Pty Limited, Australia

Reprinted in 1994 by Simon & Schuster Education

This edition published exclusively for W H Smith 1996 by
Stanley Thornes (Publishers) Ltd
Ellenborough House
Wellington Street
Cheltenham GL50 1YW

97 98 99 00 / 10 9 8 7 6

Designed by Norma van Rees
Illustrations by Boris Silvestri
Set in Plantin Light 12½/14½pt.
Printed in Great Britain by The Baskerville Press, Salisbury, Wiltshire

A catalogue record of this book is available from the British
Library

ISBN 0–7487–2105–3

Contents

Introduction

This series of four books will help to stimulate and challenge your child to think and develop mathematically, enabling them to relate mathematics to everyday life and to think logically and more strategically.

The activities, which all support National Curriculum mathematics and are excellent examples of good practice in mathematics, are graded to allow you to observe and participate in your child's development. The activities are lively and will really get your child thinking.

Here are some practical suggestions on how you can help:

- Ensure your child understands the question.

- Where do I start? Beginning is often a block for children; encourage them, pretend to be a detective and see what clues you have already.

- Encourage your child to have the confidence to have a go.

- In some of the activities there could be several solutions; let your child know that there may be many different ways to solve the question.

- Can you find a pattern? Asking your child if he/she can see any common features is a major step in mathematical thinking. Once children begin to see and explore patterns, they gain confidence and are often able to use the information gathered again in a new situation.

- Let's get organised!

  Encourage your child to put thoughts on paper, firstly so that he/she can make sense of them and, then, so that others are able to understand the notes he/she makes. This is an important aspect of mathematics. This may need some help from you. Show your child how you would set the information out: it will give clues and demonstrate the need to be systematic. Getting organised is one aspect of mathematics which will take time. . . it requires patience and understanding.

- Can you find a rule? Many of the activities in the books will encourage your child to find a rule and check whether the rule works in all cases. Encourage your child to reflect on the problem he/she has solved and to discuss what he/she has learnt from it.

- Keep a record of your child's work and look back on the progress he/she has made.

Puzzles with matches

1 This shape can be built with 12 matches.
   (a) Move 3 matches to make 3 squares all the same size.
   (b) Move 4 matches to make 3 squares of the same size.

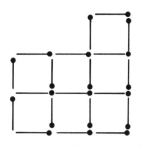

2 This shape can be built with 20 matches.
   (a) Remove 2 matches to leave 5 squares of the same size.
   (b) Remove 4 matches to leave 5 squares of the same size.
   (c) Remove 4 matches to leave 4 squares.
   (d) Move 3 matches to new positions to form 5 squares of the same size.

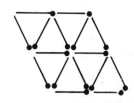

3 This shape can be built with 16 matches.
   (a) Remove 6 matches to leave 2 triangles.
   (b) Remove 4 matches to leave 6 triangles.

4 Use 9 matches to make 5 triangles.

5 Use 12 matches to make 6 triangles.

6 Make up your own puzzle.

I'M PUZZLED.

Some mathematical curiosities

3? Now that's a curious number. It was the first odd number according to the Greeks, who did not consider 1 a number.

1 Think of a number.
Multiply it by 2.
Add 5.
Multiply by 5.
Subtract 25 from this result.
Divide by 10.

Try this with different numbers. What do you find?
Why do you think this happens?

2 Think of a number.
Double it.
Add 17.
Subtract 3.
Divide by 2.
Subtract the number you first thought of.

Try this with different numbers. What do you find?
Why do you think this happens?

3 Think of a number.
Multiply it by 3.
Add 6.
Multiply by 2.
Again add 6.
Divide by 6.
Subtract 3.

Try this with different numbers. What do you find?
Try to make up one like this of your own.

4 Choose any prime number greater than 3.
Square it.
Add 5.
Divide by 12.
Write down the remainder.

Try this with different primes. What do you discover about the remainder in each case?

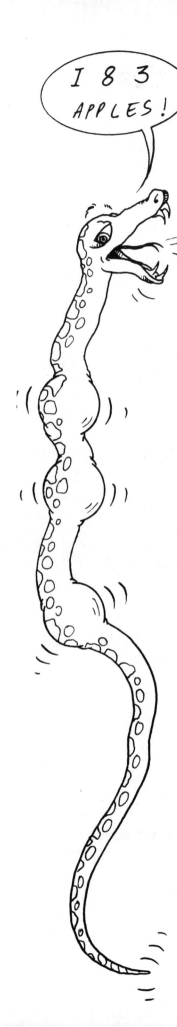

I 8 3 APPLES!

Number sentences

With the symbols $+$, $-$, $\times$, $\div$ and $(\ \ )$, and any three of the numbers 3, 4, 5, 12 and 15, complete each exercise to make it a true number sentence. You may use a number only *once* in each sentence.

Example: $12 - (15 \div 3) = 7$

1 ___ $\div$ ___ $-$ ___ $= 0$

2 ___ $\times$ ___ $-$ ___ $= 0$

3 (___ $+$ ___) $\div$ ___ $= 1$

4 (___ $-$ ___) $\div$ ___ $= 1$

5 (___ $-$ ___) $\times$ ___ $= 3$

6 (___ $+$ ___) $\div$ ___ $= 3$

7 (___ $+$ ___) $\div$ ___ $= 5$

8 ___ $\div$ ___ $+$ ___ $= 6$

9 ___ $-$ ___ $+$ ___ $= 7$

10 (___ $-$ ___) $\times$ ___ $= 8$

11 ___ $-$ (___ $\div$ ___) $= 9$

12 (___ $-$ ___) $\times$ ___ $= 9$

13 ___ $\div$ ___ $+$ ___ $= 10$

14 ___ $-$ (___ $\div$ ___) $= 11$

15 ___ $+$ ___ $+$ ___ $= 12$

16 ___ $+$ ___ $\times$ ___ $= 27$

17 ___ $\times$ ___ $+$ ___ $= 23$

18 (___ $-$ ___) $\times$ ___ $= 24$

19 (___ $+$ ___) $\times$ ___ $= 27$

20 (___ $-$ ___) $\times$ ___ $= 40$

Now try to make up one of your own that has at least 2 answers.

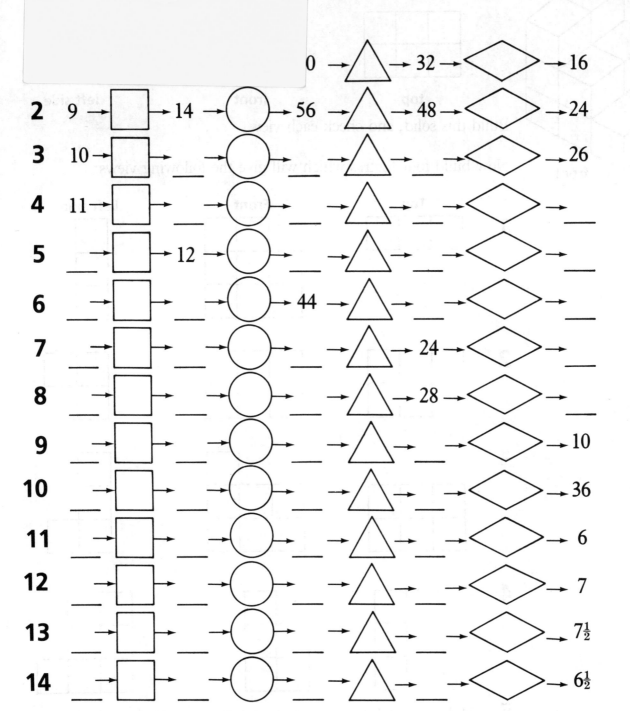

BODMAS
Brackets, order (indices)
÷ × + −

...numbers

...shapes □, ○, △ and ◇ represents a
...ation (e.g. + 7 or × 5).
...verning each shape, fill these in and work out
...numbers are.

0 → △ → 32 → ◇ → 16

2 9 → □ → 14 → ○ → 56 → △ → 48 → ◇ → 24

3 10 → □ → __ → ○ → __ → △ → __ → ◇ → 26

4 11 → □ → __ → ○ → __ → △ → __ → ◇ → __

5 __ → □ → 12 → ○ → __ → △ → __ → ◇ → __

6 __ → □ → __ → ○ → 44 → △ → __ → ◇ → __

7 __ → □ → __ → ○ → __ → △ → 24 → ◇ → __

8 __ → □ → __ → ○ → __ → △ → 28 → ◇ → __

9 __ → □ → __ → ○ → __ → △ → __ → ◇ → 10

10 __ → □ → __ → ○ → __ → △ → __ → ◇ → 36

11 __ → □ → __ → ○ → __ → △ → __ → ◇ → 6

12 __ → □ → __ → ○ → __ → △ → __ → ◇ → 7

13 __ → □ → __ → ○ → __ → △ → __ → ◇ → $7\frac{1}{2}$

14 __ → □ → __ → ○ → __ → △ → __ → ◇ → $6\frac{1}{2}$

Make up one of these of your own.

Solids

Look at the figure at left below. Beside it are shown the patterns you would see if looking from the top, from the front and from the left side.

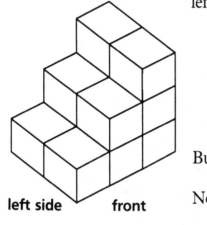

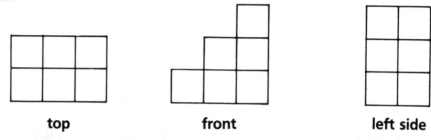

top   **front**   **left side**

Build this solid, and check each view.

Now build four figures which will give the following views:

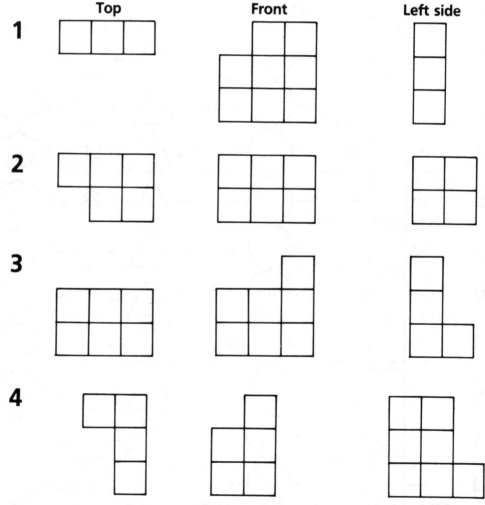

5   Make up a solid of your own and draw its top, front and left views.

Consecutive numbers

Consecutive numbers are numbers that follow in order, such as 7, 8, 9 or 11, 12, 13.

Consecutive *even* numbers are even numbers that follow in order, such as 2, 4, 6 or 22, 24.

Consecutive *odd* numbers are odd numbers that follow in order, such as 1, 3, 5 or 11, 13, 15.

1 What *consecutive* numbers are described in each case below?
  (a) Two numbers whose sum is 23.
  (b) Three numbers whose sum is 27.
  (c) Two numbers whose product is 42.
  (d) Three numbers whose product is 60.
  (e) Three even numbers whose sum is 54.
  (f) Two odd numbers whose sum is 40.
  (g) Three numbers whose sum is 75.
  (h) Three odd numbers whose sum is 75.

2 Try a lot of examples before answering these questions, and explain your reasoning.
  (a) Is the sum of two consecutive numbers always divisible by 2?
  (b) Is the product of two consecutive numbers always divisible by 2?
  (c) Is the product of three consecutive numbers always divisible by 3?
  (d) Is the product of three consecutive numbers always divisible by 6?

3 Consider three consecutive numbers. Work out the square of the middle number minus the product of the other two numbers.

For example: 4, 5, 6 $5 \times 5 - 4 \times 6$ $= 25 - 24$
                                                 $= 1$
             9, 10, 11 $10 \times 10 - 9 \times 11 = 100 - 99$
                                                 $= 1$

Try this with other numbers. What result do you find? Why?

4 Consider:
  (a) three consecutive even numbers;
  (b) three consecutive odd numbers.

  Investigate some questions of your own about numbers. The questions used above may help you find your own.

Challenge on averages

MR AVERAGE

The average of a set of numbers can be found by the following method, in which ☐ represents any number:

If you have ☐ numbers, add them together and divide the total by ☐. For example, to find the average of 3, 7, 11 and 15, ☐ = 4, since there are four numbers.

$$\therefore \text{average} = \frac{3 + 7 + 11 + 15}{4}$$

$$= \frac{36}{4}$$

$$= 9$$

1 Find the average of:
   (a) the first five consecutive numbers;
   (b) the first seven consecutive numbers;
   (c) the first nine consecutive numbers;
   (d) the first three even consecutive numbers (2, 4, 6);
   (e) the first nine even consecutive numbers.

2 Without working it out by addition and division, write down the average of the first fifteen consecutive numbers.

3 The average of five consecutive numbers is 8. What is the average of the first three of these numbers?

4 The average mass of five cases of fruit is 13 kg. The sixth case of fruit has a mass of 7 kg. What is the average mass of the six cases of fruit?

5 The average age of a group of five children is 12 years. A 24-year-old teacher joins them. What is the average age of all six?

6 The average age of five cousins is 6. If four of their ages are 7, 6, 4 and 5, what is the age of the fifth cousin?

7 In three maths tests Jeremy got 72, 78 and 80. What mark will he need in the next maths test in order to have an average score of 80 for all four?

8 The average mass of the eight members of a rowing crew is 72 kg. When the cox joins them, the average mass of crew and cox is 70 kg. Find the mass of the cox.

9 Find the average height of the children in your class.

I CHALLENGE YOU TO JUMP!

MRS AVERAGE

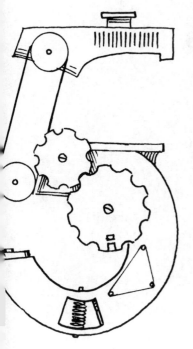

Number machine

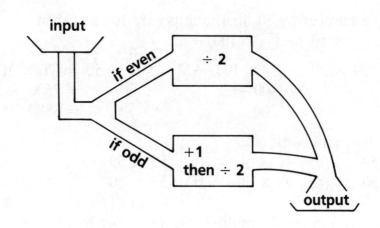

Any number — 1, 2, 3 and so on — can be fed into the number machine. One of two things will happen:

- If the input number is even, the machine will divide the number by two.
- If the input number is odd, the machine will add one to it and divide the result by two.

1 **(a)** If the input was 12, what was the output?
  (b) If the input was 11, what was the output?
  (c) If the output was 4, what are the two possible input numbers?
  (d) If the output was 7, what are the two possible input numbers?

2 Suppose you feed the output back into the input, continuing to do so until the output reaches 1.
  If you start with an input of 11, you will get
  $11 \rightarrow 6 \rightarrow 3 \rightarrow 2 \rightarrow 1$. This is a number chain.
  (a) Write down the number chain if:
    (i) you start with an input of 19;
    (ii) you start with an input of 28.
    (iii) Try your own starting inputs.
  (b) In the example above, 3 is the third-last output. What are the two possible input numbers at:
    (i) one stage before the 3?
    (ii) two stages before the 3?
    (iii) Are there always two possible input numbers? Why?

Mathematical short cuts   1

1   To multiply a number by 50, first multiply by 100 and then divide by 2: $\square \times 50 = (\square \times 100) \div 2$.

$$24 \times 50 = (24 \times 100) \div 2 \qquad 76 \times 50 = (76 \times 100) \div 2$$
$$= 2400 \div 2 \qquad\qquad = 7600 \div 2$$
$$= 1200 \qquad\qquad\quad = 3800$$

Using this short cut, work out:
(a) 14×50 (c) 42×50 (e) 55×50
(b) 36×50 (d) 98×50 (f) 59×50

2   Find your own short cut for multiplying a number by 25.
Explain why it works.

Using a short cut, work out:
(a) 12×25 (d) 36×25 (g) 18×25
(b) 16×25 (e) 9×25 (h) 21×25
(c) 28×25 (f) 10×25

3   To square a number ending in a 5, multiply the number consisting of the digit or digits in front of the 5 by 'the number itself plus 1' and write 25 at the end of your answer.

$$65 \times 65 = 6 \times 7 \text{ (hundred)} + 25 \qquad 115 \times 115 = 11 \times 12 \text{ (hundred)} + 25$$
$$= 4225 \qquad\qquad\qquad\qquad\quad = 13\,225$$

Using this short cut, work out:
(a) 25×25 (c) 55×55 (e) 105×105
(b) 35×35 (d) 75×75

4   To square a number containing $\frac{1}{2}$, such as $2\frac{1}{2}$ or $10\frac{1}{2}$, multiply the whole number by the next highest number and add $\frac{1}{4}$.

$$(2\tfrac{1}{2})^2 = 2 \times 3 + \tfrac{1}{4} \qquad (10\tfrac{1}{2})^2 = 10 \times 11 + \tfrac{1}{4}$$
$$= 6\tfrac{1}{4} \qquad\qquad\qquad = 110\tfrac{1}{4}$$

Using this short cut, work out:
(a) $(5\frac{1}{2})^2$ (c) $(9\frac{1}{2})^2$ (e) $(99\frac{1}{2})^2$
(b) $(7\frac{1}{2})^2$ (d) $(11\frac{1}{2})^2$

Mathematical short cuts 2

In these exercises you are given the patterns for short cuts, followed
by worked examples.

1 $\square^2 - \triangle^2 = (\square + \triangle) \times (\square - \triangle)$

$$7^2 - 4^2 = (7 + 4) \times (7 - 4) \qquad 97^2 - 3^2 = (97 + 3) \times (97 - 3)$$
$$= 11 \times 3 \qquad\qquad\qquad = 100 \times 94$$
$$= 33 \qquad\qquad\qquad\qquad = 9400$$

Using this short cut, work out:
- **(a)** $15^2 - 5^2$
- **(b)** $17^2 - 7^2$
- **(c)** $83^2 - 17^2$
- **(d)** $58^2 - 42^2$
- **(e)** $39^2 - 11^2$
- **(f)** $99^2 - 1^2$

2 $\square \times \bigcirc + \square \times \triangle = \square \times (\bigcirc + \triangle)$

$$5 \times 3 + 5 \times 2 = 5 \times (3 + 2) \qquad 13 \times 7 + 13 \times 3 = 13 \times (7 + 3)$$
$$= 5 \times 5 \qquad\qquad\qquad = 13 \times 10$$
$$= 25 \qquad\qquad\qquad\qquad = 130$$

Using this short cut, work out:
- **(a)** $12 \times 8 + 12 \times 2$
- **(b)** $12 \times 88 + 12 \times 12$
- **(c)** $23 \times 7 + 23 \times 3$
- **(d)** $23 \times 97 + 23 \times 3$
- **(e)** $57 \times 95 + 57 \times 5$
- **(f)** $69 \times 32 + 69 \times 68$

3 $\square \times \bigcirc - \square \times \triangle = \square \times (\bigcirc - \triangle)$

$$19 \times 18 - 19 \times 8 = 19 \times (18 - 8)$$
$$= 19 \times 10$$
$$= 190$$

Using this short cut, work out:
- **(a)** $23 \times 35 - 23 \times 15$
- **(b)** $23 \times 27 - 23 \times 17$
- **(c)** $23 \times 104 - 23 \times 4$
- **(d)** $99 \times 17 - 99 \times 7$

4 $(\bigcirc + \triangle) \times \square = \bigcirc \times \square + \triangle \times \square$
or $(\bigcirc - \triangle) \times \square = \bigcirc \times \square - \triangle \times \square$

$$102 \times 57 = (100 + 2) \times 57 \qquad\qquad 99 \times 57 = (100 - 1) \times 57$$
$$= 100 \times 57 + 2 \times 57 \qquad\qquad = 100 \times 57 - 1 \times 57$$
$$= 5700 + 114 \qquad\qquad\qquad = 5700 - 57$$
$$= 5814 \qquad\qquad\qquad\qquad = 5643$$

Using one of these short cuts, work out:
- **(a)** 103×23
- **(b)** 101×79
- **(c)** 98×23
- **(d)** 99×79

Sums the easy way

How can you quickly add the numbers from 1 to 10?
Try it yourself and then compare it with the method shown at
the bottom of the page.

1 Using a quick method, find the sums of the following numbers.
  (a) $1 + 2 + 3 + 4 + 5 + \ldots + 17 + 18 + 19 + 20$
  (b) $1 + 2 + 3 + 4 + 5 + \ldots + 95 + 96 + 97 + 98 + 99 + 100$
  (c) $1 + 2 + 3 + 4 + \ldots + 8 + 9$
  (d) $1 + 2 + 3 + 4 + \ldots + 16 + 17 + 18 + 19$
  (e) $41 + 42 + 43 + 44 + 45 + 46 + 47 + 48 + 49$
  (f) $11 + 22 + 33 + 44 + 55 + 66 + 77 + 88 + 99$
  (g) $1 + 2 + 3 + \ldots + 20 + 21 + 22$
  (h) $23 + 24 + 25 + \ldots + 72 + 73 + 74$
  (i) $2 + 4 + 6 + 8 + 10 + \ldots + 94 + 96 + 98 + 100$
  (j) $1 + 3 + 5 + 7 + 9 + \ldots + 95 + 97 + 99$

2 It is sometimes helpful to group two or three terms at a time and then add. So to
find the sum of $10 - 9 + 8 - 7 + 6 - 5 + 4 - 3 + 2 - 1$, group two terms at a
time: $(10 - 9) + (8 - 7) + (6 - 5) + (4 - 3) + (2 - 1)$
          $= 1 \quad + \quad 1 \quad + \quad 1 \quad + \quad 1 \quad + \quad 1 \quad = 5$
Using this method, find the sum of $1 - 1 + 1 - 1 + 1 - 1 + 1 - 1 + 1 - \ldots$ to
the extent of (a) 9 terms, (b) 10 terms, (c) 11 terms, (d) 20 terms, (e) 21 terms,
(f) 100 terms. Explain what you have noticed.

3 Working with the numbers $40 - 39 + 38 - 37 + 36 - 35 + 34 - 33 + \ldots$, find
sums to the extent of (a) 4 terms, (b) 6 terms, (c) 8 terms, (d) 10 terms,
(e) 20 terms, (f) 40 terms. Explain what you have noticed.

4 Find the sum of $100 - 99 + 98 - 97 + 96 - 95 + 94 - 93 + \ldots - 3 + 2 - 1$.

5 To find the sum of the numbers $1 + 3 + 5 + 7 + \ldots + 95 + 97 + 99$, it is
helpful to consider a simpler series and look for a pattern.

$$\begin{aligned} 1 + 3 &= 4 = 2^2 \\ 1 + 3 + 5 &= 9 = 3^2 \\ 1 + 3 + 5 + 7 &= 16 = ? \\ 1 + 3 + 5 + 7 + 9 &= ? = ? \end{aligned}$$

Using this method, find the sum of the odd
numbers to 100.
Note: This method is different from the one used
in exercise 1 (f).

A quick method of adding the numbers from 1 to 10 is:

$$1 + 2 + 3 + 4 + 5 + 6 + 7 + 8 + 9 + 10$$

Each pair of numbers indicated has a sum of 11.
∴ $1 + 2 + 3 + 4 + 5 + 6 + 7 + 8 + 9 + 10 = 5 \times 11 = 55$

Problem solving with a calculator

I'M GOOD AT SOLVING PROBLEMS.

1 Find two consecutive numbers whose product is:
(a) 240   (d) 1482
(b) 462   (e) 2862
(c) 1892

2 Find three consecutive numbers whose product is:
(a) 720
(b) 3360

3 Can you multiply a two-digit number by itself to give a product more than 3400 and less than 3500? If it is possible, state the number.

4 Which of these numbers is prime?
(a) 371
(b) 631

5 As I open my bedtime novel, the numbers of the two pages that face me have a product of 1332. What are the page numbers?

6 Write down any number between 100 and 999.
    Multiply it by 11.
    Multiply your answer by 91.
    What do you notice about the answer?
Repeat this procedure with several numbers.
Why does this happen?

7 Find three numbers whose sum is 16 and whose product is:
(a) 120
(b) 150
(c) 126

8 Write down any three-digit number in which all the digits are the same (e.g. 777).
    Find the sum of the digits — in this case, $7 + 7 + 7 = 21$.
    Divide the original number by this sum $(21\overline{)777})$.
    Write down your answer.
Repeat this procedure for other numbers with three identical digits. What do you find? Why?

Spirolaterals 1

Spirolaterals are patterns traced on grid paper. Imagine that a worm is programmed to crawl around a rectangular grid according to given instructions. The worm can repeat the programmed sequence as many times as it likes; however, it must turn right after each movement.

Some examples are drawn for you.

(1, 2, 3)

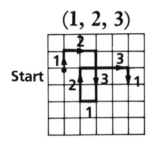

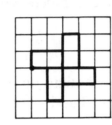

To draw a pattern, you start at a point and face 'north', or up.

For the sequence (1, 2, 3):
- move 1 unit forward, then turn right;
- move 2 units forward, then turn right;
- move 3 units forward, then turn right.

Continue to move first 1 unit, then 2, and so on until you have formed the figure shown next to the example.

Note that some spirolaterals, such as the sequences (1, 2, 3) and (2, 3), are closed, while others are open, like (1, 2, 3, 4).

(2, 3)

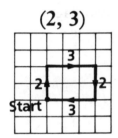

(1, 2, 3, 4)

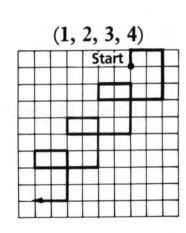

Draw the following spirolaterals. Always remember to label your patterns.

Spirolaterals have some fascinating properties: state your findings clearly, in words.

1	(1, 2)	**8**	(1, 4, 1)	**15**	(2, 4, 6, 6)
2	(3, 4)	**9**	(2, 3, 1)	**16**	(3, 1, 1, 1)
3	(1, 5)	**10**	(1, 3, 6)	**17**	(1, 3, 1, 1)
4	(1, 2, 4)	**11**	(1, 6, 3)	**18**	(6, 2, 2, 2)
5	(2, 4, 8)	**12**	(1, 2, 3, 3)	**19**	(5, 3, 1, 3)
6	(2, 3, 5)	**13**	(1, 3, 3, 5)	**20**	(5, 3, 3, 1)
7	(3, 3, 1)	**14**	(1, 5, 3, 3)	**21**	Make up your own spirolateral.

Spirolaterals 2

Draw the following spirolaterals. Always remember to label your patterns, and state clearly any properties you may find. You may need to invent some more spirolaterals of your own to test such properties.

1 (1, 2, 3, 4, 5)
2 (1, 1, 2, 3, 3)
3 (2, 2, 3, 4, 4)
4 (2, 3, 3, 1, 1)
5 (1, 2, 3, 4, 5 ...)
6 (1, 1, 2, 2, 3, 3, 4, 4 ...)
7 (3, 4, 5, 6, 7 ...)

8 (2, 4, 6, 8, 10 ...)
9 (1, 2, 3, 4, 5, 6)
10 (1, 1, 2, 2, 4, 4)
11 (1, 1, 3, 4, 1, 2)
12 (1, 2, 3, 4, 5, 6, 7)
13 (1, 2, 3, 4, 5, 6, 7, 8)
14 (1, 2, 3, 4, 5, 6, 3, 4)

The questions below may be helpful to you in identifying properties. Try to explain the results you find.

(a) What sort of patterns are formed by sequences of:
  (i) 2 terms?
  (ii) 3 terms?
  (iii) an odd number of terms?
  (iv) 4 terms?
  (v) 6 terms?
  (vi) 8 terms?

(b) What happens to the geometrical pattern if you multiply all the terms in a sequence by the same number?

Extension: Investigate spirolaterals drawn on isometric grid paper. All turns can be either 60° or 120° to the right.

Problem solving: Guess and check

1 Find two numbers:
  (a) with a sum of 12 and a product of 35;
  (b) with a sum of 12 and a product of 32;
  (c) with a sum of 15 and a product of 14;
  (d) whose sum is 76 and of which one is 12 more than the other;
  (e) whose sum is 24 and of which one is three times the other.

2 What is the largest number:
  (a) of three consecutive numbers whose sum is 21?
  (b) of three consecutive odd numbers whose sum is 27?
  Try to find a quick way of doing this.

3 **(a)** I have the same number of 10p and 50p coins. Their total value is £4.20. How many of each do I have?
  (b) I have the same number of 10p, 20p and 50p coins. Their total value is £6.40. How many of each do I have?

4 Two brothers, Khalid and Joseph, together receive £15 pocket money a month. Work out how much each boy receives if:
  (a) Khalid has £1 more than Joseph;
  (b) Khalid has £5 more than Joseph;
  (c) Khalid has £2 more than Joseph.

5 Binoculars, with their case, cost £60. If the binoculars cost £50 more than the case, how much does the case cost? (The answer is not £10.)

6 Mrs Rose has 15 flowers. She wants to place the flowers in two vases so that one vase has twice as many flowers as the other. How many flowers will there be in each vase?

7 Lisa had twice as much money as Karen. When Lisa gave Karen 5p, both had the same amount. How much did Lisa originally have?

Make up some more problems of your own.

Problem solving: Using tables

1 In a class of 30 children, it is known that there are six more boys than girls. How many girls are there in the class?

2 In a class of 30 children there are twice as many girls as boys. How many boys are there in the class?

3 (a) In a mathematics competition there are 15 problems. For every correct answer you are awarded 3 marks, but if an answer is incorrect one mark is deducted from the score.
　　If Carl attempted all 15 questions and his score was 29, how many did he answer correctly?

Answers		Total score
Correct (3 marks)	Incorrect (− 1 mark)	

(b) In another maths competition, you are awarded 5 marks for each question answered correctly and one mark is deducted for an incorrect answer.
　　If there are 30 questions in the competition, a student attempts all 30 and receives 108 marks, how many of the student's answers were wrong?

4 Amanda has 20 coins in her purse. She has only 10p, 20p and 50p coins, and their total value is £5
　　If she has more 50p than 10p coins, how many 10p coins has she?

5 Gus, Verid and their three children went to the circus. The children were charged half-price.
　　If the total cost of the tickets was £31.50, how much did each adult ticket cost?

6 Julian's age has the same figures as his dad's with the digits reversed. The sum of their ages is 99 and Julian is 27 years younger than his dad.
　　How old is Julian?

Problem solving: All the possibilities

1 Andrew, Benjamin, Coreen, Devorah and Eileen are nominated for the positions of school captain and vice-captain.

   (a) List the different ways in which (i) the school captain can be elected; (ii) both captain and vice-captain can be elected.

       Note that electing Coreen captain and Benjamin vice-captain is different from electing Benjamin vice-captain and Coreen captain.

         Use the initials A, B, C, D and E to list the possibilities. It may be helpful to use a tree diagram.

   (b) If Coreen decided not to stand, in how many different ways could (i) the captain be elected? (ii) both captain and vice-captain be elected?

2 Three girls (Nicole, Irene and Kathy) and three boys (Dimitry, Victor and Russell) audition for parts in a play that requires a queen and a king.

   (a) List the different queen–king pairs that can be chosen.

   (b) Irene decides she no longer wishes to audition for the queen's part. List the possible queen–king pairs.

   (c) Joseph decides that he would like to audition as well, so now two girls and four boys are trying out for the play.

       List the possible queen–king pairs.

   (d) By completing this table, work out how many different queen–king pairs are possible in each instance.

Students auditioning		Queen–king pairs
Girls	**Boys**	
1	2	
2	2	
2	3	
3	2	
3	3	
3	4	
4	3	
4	4	
4	5	
5	5	
5	6	
6	6	

Problem solving: Working backwards

NOW WHAT'S THE QUESTION?

Try to solve these problems by working from the end to the beginning. Try to explain your way of solving these problems.

1 Find the hidden numbers that fulfil the following conditions:
  (a) If you add 4 to the number and double the result, you get 20.
  (b) If you double the number, double that result and then double again, you get 16.
  (c) If you subtract 4 from the number and halve the result, you get 6.
  (d) If you multiply the number by 5, subtract 3 and halve the result, you get 6.
  (e) If you subtract 5, square the result and then add 8, you get 17.
  (f) If you multiply the number by 4, subtract 10 and divide the result by 5, you get 2.

2 Anthony receives his weekly pocket money every Monday. On one Tuesday, he spends 75p. On Wednesday he buys a magazine for £1.25. On Thursday he finds a 50p coin in the street, which means he then has £2.

How much is Anthony's pocket money?

3 Tahli has to be at school by 8.30 a.m. It takes her 10 minutes to walk there from home. Eating breakfast takes 15 minutes, dressing takes 10 minutes, practising the piano 15 minutes and cleaning her room 5 minutes.

What time must she get out of bed?

4 Daniel played a card game in which each loss meant that he had to give the other player half the cards he had left. He lost four times, one after the other, and then had 3 cards left.

How many cards did he have when he started?

Investigations with lines

Lines drawn in exactly the same direction will never meet, and are called *parallel*.

Here are four examples of parallel lines:

 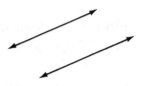 

Three straight lines drawn on a sheet of paper can:

- all be parallel and never intersect
- intersect in 2 points (if two of the lines are parallel)
- intersect in 1 point
- intersect in 3 points

  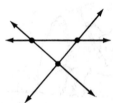

1 Investigate the possible ways you can draw four straight lines.

2 Investigate the possible ways you can draw five straight lines.

 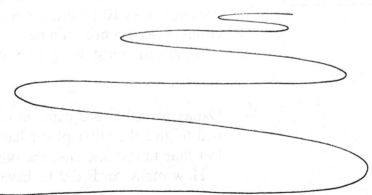

How many diagonals?

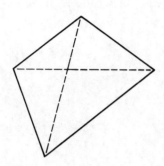

A diagonal is a straight line drawn from one vertex of a polygon (figure) to another vertex that is not next to the first one. A vertex of a polygon is a corner (the plural of the word 'vertex' is 'vertices').

In this figure, the diagonals are the dotted lines.

1 Count the number of diagonals that can be drawn in each figure and complete the table below them. Look for patterns, and express in words those you find.

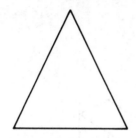

3 sides

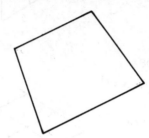

4 sides

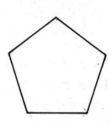

5 sides

6 sides

7 sides

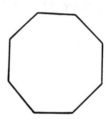

8 sides

Number of sides	3	4	5	6	7	8 →
Number of vertices	3	4				
Diagonals at each vertex	0	1				
Total diagonals	0					

2 Without counting the diagonals, predict the number of diagonals for:
(a) a nine-sided figure (a nonagon);
(b) a ten-sided figure (a decagon).

Cube explorations

1 Examine the solid at right.
  - **(a)** How many small cubes are needed to build it?
  - **(b)** How many small cubes can you actually see in this view?
  - **(c)** How many small cubes cannot be seen in this view?

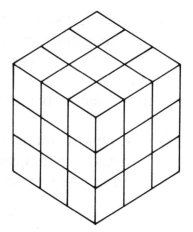

2 Now look at the second large cube.
  - **(a)** How many small cubes are needed to build it?
  - **(b)** How many small cubes can you see in this view?
  - **(c)** How many small cubes are hidden in this view?

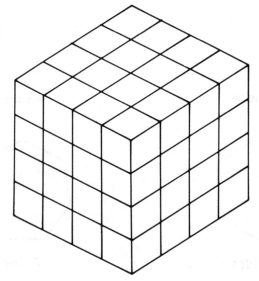

3 A block of cheese is covered with wax and then cut into 1 cm cubes. Given the measurements of the cheese, complete this table to show in each case (a) how many cubes can be cut, (b) how many cubes will have wax on them and (c) how many will not have wax on them.

Size of cheese	Cubes cut	Cubes with wax	Cubes without wax
3 cm × 3 cm × 3 cm			
4 cm × 4 cm × 4 cm			
5 cm × 5 cm × 5 cm			
6 cm × 6 cm × 6 cm			

Mathematics is amazing

You can use your calculator for these exercises.

1 Two examples of four-digit palindromic numbers are 1551 and 7447. Both these numbers are divisible by 11.
Investigate!

2 **(a)** Write down a three-digit number in which the digits are all different, such as 635.
Now write down all the possible two-digit combinations of the three digits you used, and add them together:
$$63 + 65 + 35 + 36 + 56 + 53 = 308$$

Note that you should always have six possibilities. Why?
Add the digits in the original number:
$$635 \rightarrow 6 + 3 + 5 = 14$$

Now divide the sum of the two-digit numbers (in this case, 308) by the sum of digits in the original number (in this case, 14).
$$308 \div 14 = 22$$

Investigate this procedure using other three-digit numbers.

(b) Try this with three-digit numbers in which two of the digits are repeated, as in 363.
Note that there will be only three possible combinations of two digits, in this case:
$$33 + 63 + 36$$

True or false?

Here are sixty number sentences. Check each one carefully to see whether it is true or false.

1 $(3 + 4) + 5 = 3 + (4 + 5)$

2 $(3 \times 4) + 5 = 3 \times (4 + 5)$

3 $(2 \times 3) \times 4 = 2 \times (3 \times 4)$

4 $(5 - 3) + 2 = 5 - (3 + 2)$

5 $(8 - 3) \times 2 = 8 - (3 \times 2)$

6 $(4 + 8) \times 2 = 4 + (8 \times 2)$

7 $3 \times 7 = 7 \times 3$

8 $4 \div 2 = 2 \div 4$

9 $(5 - 3) - 2 = 5 - (3 - 2)$

10 $(24 \div 6) - 4 = 24 \div (6 - 4)$

11 $(3 \times 10) \div 2 = 3 \times (10 \div 2)$

12 $6 \div 3 = 6 \times \frac{1}{3}$

13 $\frac{1}{2}$ of $14 = 14 \div 2$

14 $\frac{1}{2}$ of $20 = 20 \times \frac{1}{2}$

15 $\frac{1}{2}$ of $4 + \frac{1}{2}$ of $6 = \frac{1}{2}$ of $(4 + 6)$

16 $\frac{1}{2}$ of $12 + \frac{1}{2}$ of $4 = \frac{1}{2}$ of 16

17 $\frac{1}{4}$ of $12 + \frac{1}{4}$ of $12 = \frac{1}{2}$ of 12

18 $\frac{1}{4}$ of $16 + \frac{1}{4}$ of $16 = (\frac{1}{4} + \frac{1}{4})$ of 16

19 $2^2 = 2 \times 2$

20 $3^2 + 4^2 = 5^2$

21 $2^2 + 3^2 = (2 + 3)^2$

22 $4^3 = 4 \times 4 \times 4$

23 $4^3 - 4^2 = 4$

24 $4^3 \div 4^2 = 4$

25 $9^2 - 2^2 = (9 - 2) \times (9 + 2)$

26 $10^2 - 5^2 = (10 - 5) \times (10 + 5)$

27 $9^2 - 3^2 = 6 \times 12$

28 $8^2 - 2^2 = 6 \times 10$

29 $7^2 - 3^2 = 4^2$

30 $100^2 - 1^2 = 101 \times 99$

31 $4 \times 9 - 4 \times 4 = 4 \times (9 - 4)$

32 $(12 - 5) \times 2 = 12 \times 2 - 5 \times 2$

33 $8 \times 3 - 5 \times 3 = (8 - 5) \times 3$

34 $3 \times 4 + 2 \times 4 = (3 + 2) \times 4$

35 $99 \times 7 + 99 \times 3 = 99 \times (7 + 3)$

36 $(30 \div 5) + (20 \div 5) = 50 \div 5$

37 $(30 \div 5) - (20 \div 5) = 10 \div 5$

38 $(12 \div 4) + (8 \div 4) = (12 + 8) \div 4$

39 $(20 \div 2) + (12 \div 2) = (20 + 12) \div 2$

40 $(3 + 4)^2 = 3^2 + 4^2 + 2 \times 3 \times 4$

41 $(5 + 2)^2 = 5^2 + 2^2$

42 $(5 + 2)^2 = 5^2 + 2^2 + 2 \times 5 \times 2$

43 $\frac{1}{3} < \frac{1}{4}$

44 $(\frac{1}{2})^2 < \frac{1}{4}$

45 $(\frac{1}{2})^2 < \frac{1}{2}$

46 $-5 > -4$

47 $-9 < -8$

48 $-9 > 0$

49 $-1 < 0$

50 $-1 + 1 = 0$

51 $-4 + 4 = 0$

52 $-3 + 9 = 6$

53 $0.4 < 4.0$

54 $(0.2)^2 = 0.4$

55 $0.4 \times 0.3 = 1.2$

56 $(0.5)^2 = 0.25$

57 $\triangle^2 = \triangle \times \triangle$

58 $(\triangle + \bigcirc) + \square = \triangle + (\bigcirc + \square)$

59 $\triangle^2 + \bigcirc^2 = (\triangle + \bigcirc)^2$

60 $\triangle - \bigcirc - \square = \triangle - (\bigcirc + \square)$

Repeating cycles

If you take the number 1, double it, double it again and then again and so continue doubling, you will get the sequence:
1, 2, 4, 8, 16, 32, 64, 128, 256 ...

If you now write down the end (unit) digits of this sequence, you will have:
1, 2, 4, 8, 6, 2, 4, 8, 6 ...

These unit digits form a pattern of repeating cycles:

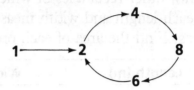

1 **(a)** If you start with 3 and keep doubling, you will get the sequence:
3, 6, 12, 24, 48, 96, 192, 384, 768 ...

If you then write down the unit digits of this sequence, you will have:
3, 6, 2, 4, 8, 6, 2, 4, 8 ...

Draw the repeating cycle for this sequence.

(b) Draw the repeating cycle of unit digits starting with 4, 5, 6, 7, 8, 9 and 10, and repeating the doubling procedure.

(c) Explain what you have found.

2 **(a)** If you start with 4 and write down the multiples of 4, you will get the sequence:
4, 8, 12, 16, 20, 24, 28, 32, 36, 40, 44 ...

If you now write down the unit digits of this sequence, you will have:
4, 8, 2, 6, 0, 4, 8, 2, 6, 0, 4 ...

Draw the repeating cycle for this sequence.

(b) The multiples of 2 are 2, 4, 6, 8 ...; the multiples of 3 are 3, 6, 9, 12 ... and the multiples of 5 are 5, 10, 15, 20 ...

Investigate the repeating cycle of unit digits with multiples of 2, 3, 5, 6, 7, 8 and 9.

(c) Describe any interesting patterns you see.

Area and perimeter investigations

1 Two possible rectangles having a perimeter of 16 metres are these:

1 m [rectangle] 7 m

2 m [rectangle] 6 m

Draw other rectangles of which each perimeter is 16 metres and each length and width measures a whole number of metres. Find the area of each one, and complete this table:

Length (m)	Width (m)	Area (m²)
7	1	7
6	2	

Which shape gives you the largest area? Why does that happen?

2 Repeat the above exercise to construct rectangles with a perimeter measure of:

(a) 20 metres   **(b)** 24 metres

Set your work out in a table and explain your findings.

3 The area of a rectangle is 24 m² and its length and width each measure a whole number of metres. On squared paper, draw as many different rectangles as you can which will fulfil these conditions, and find the perimeter of each one.

Then complete this table:

Length (m)	Width (m)	Perimeter (m)
24	1	

Which shape gives you the smallest perimeter?

4 The area of a rectangle is:

(a) 36 m²   **(b)** 100 m²   **(c)** choose your own.

The length and the width each measure a whole number of metres.

Draw up a table to show the different rectangles that can be drawn to the given measurements. Find the shape that gives you the smallest perimeter in each case.

Finding areas

1 A rectangular pool measures 12 metres by 8 metres and is bordered by a concrete path 2 metres wide, as shown.

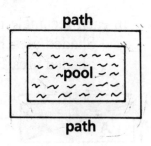

How many square metres are in the surface area of the concrete path?

There are lots of ways of finding this out. Try and find more than one way and then choose the one you think is best.

2 The measurements of a garden are shown below. Find the area of the garden in three different ways by considering the areas of the rectangles indicated by the dotted lines.

(a) Find area A + area B.

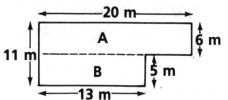

(b) Find area C + area D.

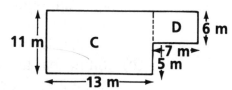

(c) Find the area of the large rectangle (11 m × 20 m) minus the area of E.

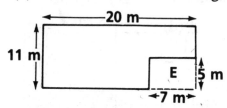

3 Find the area of a room at your school or at home.

Area of triangles

1   In each rectangle below:

　　Shaded area B = unshaded area A

　　∴ Shaded area B = ½ area of rectangle

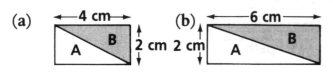 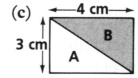 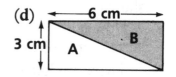

What is the area of the shaded triangle in each figure?

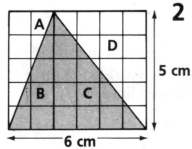

2   In the rectangle on the left:

Shaded area B	= unshaded area A
Shaded area C	= unshaded area D
∴ Shaded area (B + C)	= unshaded area (A + D)
∴ Shaded area (B + C)	= ½ area of rectangle

(a)   Show that these statements are true by copying this diagram onto squared paper, cutting out the four triangles and fitting the shapes one on top of another as required.

(b)   Show that the statements are true by first working out the areas of triangles A, B, C and D.

3   Find the area of the shaded triangle in each of these figures:

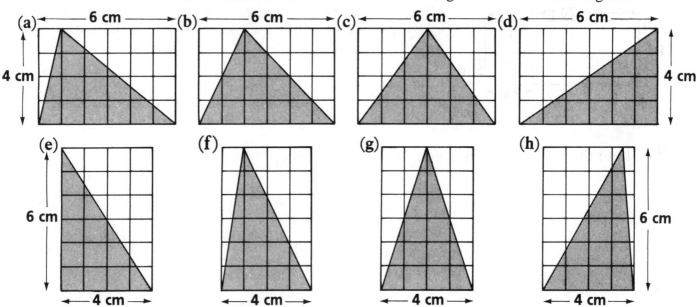

Investigate the areas of triangles drawn in rectangles in this way.

4   Draw some triangles with areas of 12 cm².

Problem solving: Organising lists 1

1 In how many ways can you change a £1 coin into 50p, 20p and 10p coins?
Illustrate this in a table.

50p	20p	10p
2	–	–
1	2	1

2 Debbie asks a shop keeper to change 50p into 20p, 10p and 5p coins only.

(a) Complete this table to list all possible ways in which she could be given change.

20p	10p	5p
2	1	

(b) Work out how many coins of each value the shopkeeper would give Debbie if he gave her:
(i) 5 coins   (ii) 7 coins   (iii) 8 coins

3 Anne, Betty, Carol and Dora are nominated for the positions of class captain and vice-captain. Use the girls' initials only (A, B, C and D), and find out how many different ways this selection can be made. Show these on a diagram.

4 Mr Helpful is making the children's sandwiches in the morning. He plans to use white bread or brown bread and the fillings he has available are egg, cheese, tuna and honey. List the various sandwiches he can make if he puts only one type of filling in each sandwich. Show these on a diagram.

5 A group of girls enters a tennis tournament. Each player plays every other competitor once.
    Work out how many games must be played if the tournament is entered by:
(a) 3 girls   **(c)** 5 girls
(b) 4 girls   **(d)** 6 girls
List the players as A, B, C and so on.
Now look for a pattern in your findings.
(e) Can you predict how many games must be played in a tournament entered by 10 girls?

Problem solving: Organising lists 2

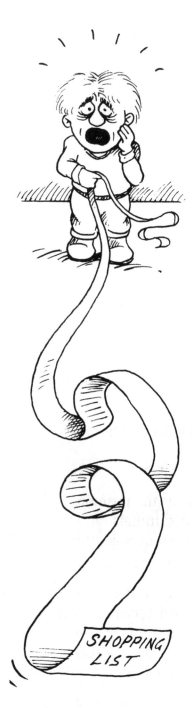

Drawing up a table may help in most of these problems.
In each case find as many solutions as you can.

1 **(a)** Hans ordered 15 pikelets, which are packaged in sets of three or four. In how many ways can the order be filled?

(b) Later, Hans ordered 23 pikelets from a different company, where pikelets are packaged in sets of three, four or five. In how many ways can Hans' order be filled this time?

Sets of 3	Sets of 4	Sets of 5

2 Giovanni needs exactly 17 kg of pasta for his restaurant this week. At the supermarket, pasta can be bought in 3 kg packages for £4.20 each or in 5 kg packages for £6.50 each.

How many packages of each size must Giovanni select in order to obtain the best buy?

3 kg packages at £4.20	5 kg packages at £6.50	Total cost

3 Most banks charge £2.50 for a cheque book with 25 cheques in it. However, as a promotion to attract customers, a new bank is advertising a monthly service charge of £1.50 plus 5 pence for each cheque you use.

How many cheques would you need to use each month in order to save money with the new plan?

Number of cheques	Usual charge	New charge

4 Which weekly pocket-money system would you prefer?
(a) £1.10 a week
(b) 1p the 1st day
2p the 2nd day
4p the 3rd day
8p the 4th day
and so on for 7 days.

5 During the debating season, seven schools enter a competition. Each is scheduled to debate with every other school once.

How many debates are scheduled for the competition?

Problem solving: Listing possibilities

In each case describe how you attempted the problem.

1 **(a)** In a lighthouse there are two lights, X and Y.
Light X flashes every 2 minutes.
Light Y flashes every 5 minutes.
At 9 p.m. they flashed together. At what time will this happen again?

(b) The lights are adjusted at 10 p.m., at which time they flashed together, but now light X flashes every 6 minutes and light Y every 10 minutes.
At what time will they next flash together?

(c) Lights X and Y flash together at 11 p.m. Complete the following table to show each time they would next flash together if set at the frequencies given.

	Time between flashes		Next flash together
	Light X	**Light Y**	
(i)	3 min.	5 min.	
(ii)	3 min.	7 min.	
(iii)	4 min.	10 min.	
(iv)	4 min.	11 min.	
(v)	4 min.	12 min.	
(vi)	5 min.	12 min.	
(vii)	5 min.	15 min.	
(viii)	6 min.	7 min.	
(ix)	6 min.	15 min.	

2 Anatoly is playing a board game where he has to roll two dice.
(a) What is the smallest sum that he can roll?
(b) With how many combinations can he roll:
(i) a sum of 8? (ii) a sum of 12?
(c) Which sum has the most possible combinations?
(d) Explore what happens with 3 dice.

3 In an old-fashioned cuckoo clock, the bird cuckoos once at 1 o'clock, twice at 2 o'clock, three times at 3 o'clock and so on. Jamie, who is at home sick, wakes just before 7 a.m. and goes to sleep at 8:15 p.m. How many times has the bird called during this period?

Area investigation   1

Investigate what happens to the area of various shapes if the length of each side is doubled.

For each exercise, draw diagrams on squared paper to work out your answers and to illustrate your work. Then complete the tables.

1   Squares

Original side (cm)	Original area (cm²)	Enlarged side (cm)	Enlarged area (cm²)
3	9	6	
4	16	8	
5			
6			
7			

How many times bigger than the original area is the new area? Express your finding clearly in words and explain what you think has happened.

2   Rectangles

Original length and breadth (cm)		Original area (cm²)	Enlarged length and breadth (cm)		Enlarged area (cm²)
2	1	2	4	2	
3	2	6			
4	3				
5	2				

How many times bigger than the original area is the new area?

3   Triangles (right-angled) All measurements are in centimetres.
Find the area of each right-angled triangle and complete the table below.

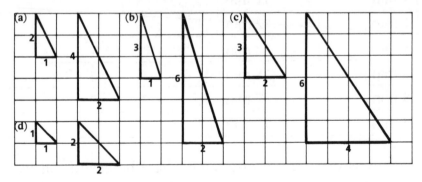

	Original base and height (cm)		Original area (cm²)	Enlarged base and height (cm)		Enlarged area (cm²)
(a)	1	2	1	2	4	
(b)	1	3	1½	2	6	
(c)	2	3		4	6	
(d)	1	1		2	2	

How many times bigger than the original area is the new area?

4   Investigate this property with other shapes.

Area investigation   2

1   What happens to the area of some figures if the sides are trebled (multiplied by 3)?
Consider these figures:

(a) squares   **(b)** a rectangle

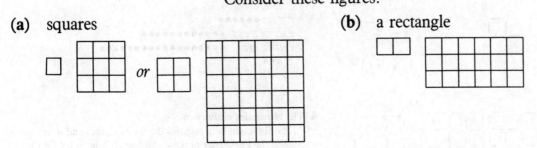

How many times bigger than the original area is the new area?
Experiment with triangles and other shapes.

2   In each section below, the length of the sides of a shape is multiplied by 2, 3 and 4. Write down, in each case, by how much each of the enlarged shapes is bigger than the first figure. Predict how much bigger they are for lengths 10 times longer.
Express your findings in words.

(a) triangle

(b) rhombus

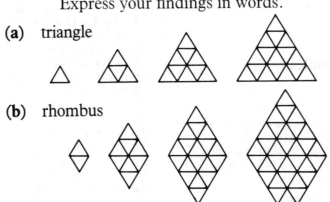

(c) parallelogram

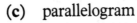
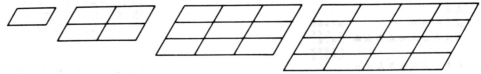

(d) trapezium (isosceles)

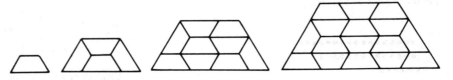

Solutions Book D

Puzzles with matches (page 6)

1 Matches in new positions are shown with heavier lines.

(a) (b) **2**(a)

(b) (c)

(d) **3**(a) (b)

4 This is a tricky question, as not all the triangles are the same size. If the children become frustrated, this can be given as a hint.

5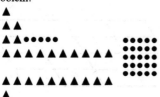

Some mathematical curiosities (page 7)

Children will be fascinated with these problems. After trying several different numbers, they can justify the results by using concrete material such as centicubes for the original numbers and counters for the additional numbers. Children should be encouraged to explain their results in their own way using words or symbols. The ones shown here are just one possible way of thinking about these problems.

1 The result is the number you first thought of.
Let the original number be ▲. Now, working through the problem:

2 The result is always 7.
Let the original number be □:

3 The result is the number you first thought of.
Let the original number be □:

4 The remainder is always 6.
The argument here requires the use of algebra and so is beyond the knowledge of these children. It is included for the teacher's interest:

Any prime number greater than 3 is of the form $6n \pm 1$ ($\pm$ means 'plus or minus'), where n is a whole number.
On squaring, the number is of the form:
$$36n^2 \pm 12n + 1$$
Add 5: $36n^2 \pm 12n + 6$
Dividing by 12, the remainder is always 6.

Number sentences (page 8)

These are some possible answers.
1 $15 \div 5 - 3 = 0$ *or* $12 \div 4 - 3 = 0$
2 $4 \times 3 - 12 = 0$ *or* $3 \times 5 - 15 = 0$
3 $(12 + 3) \div 15 = 1$
4 $(15 - 12) \div 3 = 1$
5 $(5 - 4) \times 3 = 3$
6 $(5 + 4) \div 3 = 3$ *or* $(12 + 3) \div 5 = 3$
7 $(15 + 5) \div 4 = 5$
8 $15 \div 5 + 3 = 6$ *or* $12 \div 4 + 3 = 6$
9 $15 - 12 + 4 = 7$
10 $(5 - 3) \times 4 = 8$
11 $12 - (15 \div 5) = 9$
12 $(15 - 12) \times 3 = 9$
13 $15 \div 3 + 5 = 10$
14 $15 - (12 \div 3) = 11$
15 $3 + 4 + 5 = 12$
16 $5 + 4 \times 3 = 27$
17 $4 \times 5 + 3 = 23$
18 $(12 - 4) \times 3 = 24$ *or* $(5 - 3) \times 12 = 24$
19 $(5 + 4) \times 3 = 27$
20 $(12 - 4) \times 5 = 40$ *or* $(15 - 5) \times 4 = 40$

Missing numbers (page 9)

From 1 and 2, the rule for each shape can be found:

Children first have to apply the rule to the starting numbers. In the last ten questions they will have to employ the strategy 'working backwards'. This is an excellent exercise in the use of this method.

3 10, 15, 60, 52, 26   **9** 2, 7, 28, 20, 10
4 11, 16, 64, 56, 28   **10** 15, 20, 80, 72, 36
5 7, 12, 48, 40, 20   **11** 0, 5, 20, 12, 6
6 6, 11, 44, 36, 18   **12** ½, 5½ = ⁹⁄₂, 22, 14, 7
7 3, 8, 32, 24, 12   **13** ¾, 5¾ = ²³⁄₄, 23, 15, 7½
8 4, 9, 36, 28, 14   **14** ¼, 5¼ = ²¹⁄₄, 21, 13, 6½

Solids (page 10)

It is important that children build the solid given in the example and check each view. In fact, they could try to build the solid from only the given views, with the example covered.

They should be encouraged to find their own way of building the solids. One way is to first lay the base of each one to look the same as the view from the top, then build the front view and check the view from the left.

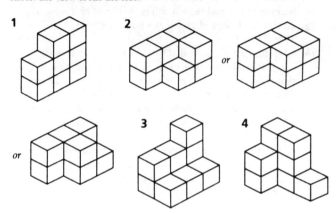

Consecutive numbers (page 11)

1 (a) 11, 12
  (b) 8, 9, 10
  (c) 6, 7
  (d) 3, 4, 5
  (e) 16, 18, 20
  (f) 19, 21
  (g) 24, 25, 26
  (h) 23, 25, 27

There are two methods by which we can solve these problems.
(i) Use trial and error, drawing up a table if necessary.
(ii) In (a), (c) and (f), if the sum is halved we get an approximation, and the two numbers are the one before and the one after it:
    23 ÷ 2 = 11½, so the numbers are 11 and 12.
    In (b), (d), (e), (g) and (h), if we divide the number by 3, we get the middle number.

2 (a) The sum of two consecutive numbers is not divisible by 2, as one of the numbers is always odd and one is always even (e.g. 5 and 6 or 6 and 7), and the sum of an even and an odd number is always odd.
  (b) Since an even number times an odd number is even, the product is divisible by 2.
  (c) Of 3 consecutive numbers, one will always be a multiple of 3; therefore, the product will be divisible by 3 (e.g. 4 × 5 × 6 or 3 × 4 × 5).
  (d) Yes, since from (c), above, the product is always divisible by 3; and since the product of any two consecutive numbers is divisible by 2, the product will be divisible by 2 and 3, which is 6.

3 For three consecutive numbers, the square of the middle number minus the product of the other two numbers will always be 1.
4 (a, b) It is very important to help children ask their own questions. One interesting finding is that . . . for both consecutive even and consecutive odd numbers, the square of the middle number minus the product of the other two numbers will always be 4.

Examples:
    4, 6, 8   10, 12, 14   3, 5, 7
 36 − 32 = 4 144 − 140 = 4 25 − 21 = 4

      11, 13, 15
    169 − 165 = 4

Challenge on averages (page 12)

1 (a) Average of 1, 2, 3, 4, 5 is 3,
    since 1 + 2 + 3 + 4 + 5 = 15
         and 15 ÷ 5 = 3.
  (b) Average of 1, 2, 3, 4, 5, 6, 7 is 4.
  (c) Average of 1, 2, 3, 4, 5, 6, 7, 8, 9 is 5.
  (d) Average of 2, 4, 6 is 4. *Note*: It is the middle number.
  (e) Average of 2, 4, 6, 8, 10, 12, 14, 16, 18 is 10. *Note*: It is the middle number.

2 Average of 1, 2, 3 → 15 is the middle number, which is 8.

3 First write down the five consecutive numbers. Using the above formula, the numbers are 6, 7, 8, 9, 10, the average being the middle number. Therefore, the first three are 6, 7, 8, and their average is 7.

4 Since the average mass of the five cases of fruit is 13 kg, the total mass of the five cases is 5 × 13 = 65 kg. With the sixth case, the total mass becomes 72 kg. Therefore, the average mass of the six cases is 72 ÷ 6 = 12 kg.

5 Total age of children   = 5 × 12
                     = 60
    Total age with teacher = 60 + 24
                     = 84
    ∴ Average age of the six = 84 ÷ 6
                     = 14

6 If the average age of five cousins is 6, the total age is 30. The sum of the four given ages is 22; therefore, the fifth cousin is 8 years old.

7 If the average for four tests is 80, the total score is 320. Therefore, 90 marks are still needed.

8 Total mass of the rowing crew = 8 × 72
                         = 576 kg
    Total mass of crew plus cox = 9 × 70
                         = 630 kg
    ∴ Weight of cox   = 54 kg

Number machine (page 13)

1 (a) 6 **(b)** 6 **(c)** 8 or 7 **(d)** 14 or 13

2 (a) (i) $19 \to 10 \to 5 \to 3 \to 2 \to 1$

(ii) $28 \to 14 \to 7 \to 4 \to 2 \to 1$

(b) (i) 5 or 6

(ii)

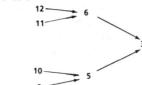

Mathematical short cuts 1 (page 14)

1 (a) $1400 \div 2 = 700$ **(d)** $9800 \div 2 = 4900$

(b) $3600 \div 2 = 1800$ **(e)** $5500 \div 2 = 2750$

(c) $4200 \div 2 = 2100$ **(f)** $5900 \div 2 = 2950$

2 To multiply by 25, first multiply by 100 and then divide by 4.

(a) $1200 \div 4 = 300$ **(e)** $900 \div 4 = 225$

(b) $1600 \div 4 = 400$ **(f)** $1000 \div 4 = 250$

(c) $2800 \div 4 = 700$ **(g)** $1800 \div 4 = 450$

(d) $3600 \div 4 = 900$ **(h)** $2100 \div 4 = 525$

3 (a) $2 \times 3 \text{ (hundred)} + 25 = 625$

(b) $3 \times 4 \text{ (hundred)} + 25 = 1225$

(c) $5 \times 6 \text{ (hundred)} + 25 = 3025$

(d) $7 \times 8 \text{ (hundred)} + 25 = 5625$

(e) $10 \times 11 \text{ (hundred)} + 25 = 11\,025$

4 (a) $5 \times 6 + \frac{1}{4} = 30\frac{1}{4}$ **(d)** $11 \times 12 + \frac{1}{4} = 132\frac{1}{4}$

(b) $7 \times 8 + \frac{1}{4} = 56\frac{1}{4}$ **(e)** $99 \times 100 + \frac{1}{4} = 9900\frac{1}{4}$

(c) $9 \times 10 + \frac{1}{4} = 90\frac{1}{4}$

Mathematical short cuts 2 (page 15)

1 (a) $(15 + 5) \times (15 - 5) = 20 \times 10$
$$= 200$$

(b) $(17 + 7) \times (17 - 7) = 24 \times 10$
$$= 240$$

(c) $(83 + 17) \times (83 - 17) = 100 \times 66$
$$= 6600$$

(d) $(58 + 42) \times (58 - 42) = 100 \times 16$
$$= 1600$$

(e) $(39 + 11) \times (39 - 11) = 50 \times 28$
$$= 1400$$

(f) $(99 + 1) \times (99 - 1) = 100 \times 98$
$$= 9800$$

2 (a) $12 \times (8 + 2) = 120$ **(d)** $23 \times (97 + 3) = 2300$

(b) $12 \times (88 + 12) = 1200$ **(e)** $57 \times (95 + 5) = 5700$

(c) $23 \times (7 + 3) = 230$ **(f)** $69 \times (32 + 68) = 6900$

3 (a) $23 \times (35 - 15) = 460$ **(c)** $23 \times (104 - 4) = 2300$

(b) $23 \times (27 - 17) = 230$ **(d)** $99 \times (17 - 7) = 990$

4 (a) $(100 + 3) \times 23 = 2300 + 69 = 2369$

(b) $(100 + 1) \times 79 = 100 \times 79 + 1 \times 79 = 7979$

(c) $(100 - 2) \times 23 = 100 \times 23 - 2 \times 23$
$$= 2300 - 46 = 2254$$

(d) $(100 - 1) \times 79 = 100 \times 79 - 1 \times 79$
$$= 7900 - 79 = 7821$$

Sums the easy way (page 16)

Encourage children to try their own methods first.

1 (a) 20 terms: 10 pairs of numbers whose sum is $21 = 10 \times 21$
$$= 210$$

(b) 100 terms:
50 pairs of numbers whose sum is $101 = 50 \times 101$
$$= 5050$$

(c) 9 terms: 4 pairs of numbers whose sum is 10, plus the number in the middle $= 4 \times 10 + 5 = 45$

(d) 19 terms: 9 pairs of numbers whose sum is 20, plus the number in the middle $= 9 \times 20 + 10 = 190$

(e) 9 terms: 4 pairs of numbers whose sum is 90, plus the number in the middle $= 4 \times 90 + 45 = 405$

(f) 9 terms: 4 pairs of numbers whose sum is 110, plus the number in the middle $= 4 \times 110 + 55 = 495$

(g) 22 terms: 11 pairs of numbers whose sum is $23 = 11 \times 23 = 253$

(h) 52 terms (not 51, as both 23 and 74 are included in the sum). Possibly the easiest way to work this out is to say that there are 22 terms in the sum $1 + 2 + \ldots + 22$ and 74 terms in the sum $1 + 2 + 3 + \ldots + 73 + 74$; therefore there are 52 terms in the sum $23 + 24 + \ldots + 73 + 74$, and 26 pairs of numbers whose sum is 97 $= 26 \times 97 = 2522$.

Alternatively, first find the sum of the numbers from 1 to 74, which is 37 pairs whose sum is 75, and $37 \times 75 = 2775$. Now subtract the sum of the numbers from 1 to 22, in (g): $23 + 24 + \ldots + 73 + 74 = 2775 - 253$
$$= 2522$$

(i) 50 terms: 25 pairs of numbers whose sum is $102 = 25 \times 102 = 2550$

(j) 50 terms: 25 pairs of numbers whose sum is $100 = 25 \times 100 = 2500$

2 (a) 1   **(d)** 0   If we add an even number of terms the answer is 0, and if we add an odd number the answer is 1.

(b) 0   **(e)** 1

(c) 1   **(f)** 0

3 (a) 2   **(d)** 5   If we add an even number of terms, the answer is half of the number of terms being added, as each pair of numbers has a sum of 1.

(b) 3   **(e)** 10

(c) 4   **(f)** 20

4 50

5
$$1 + 3 = 4 = 2^2 \text{ (2 terms)}$$
$$1 + 3 + 5 = 9 = 3^2 \text{ (3 terms)}$$
$$1 + 3 + 5 + 7 = 16 = 4^2 \text{ (4 terms)}$$
$$1 + 3 + 5 + 7 + 9 = 25 = 5^2 \text{ (5 terms)}$$
$$1 + 3 + 5 + 7 + 9 + \ldots + 99 = 50^2 \text{ (50 terms)}$$
$$= 2500$$

Problem solving with a calculator (page 17)

1 (a) Children may use trial and error. However, another good strategy for approximation is to find the square root of the number; $\sqrt{240} \doteq 15.49$, so the two consecutive numbers are 15 and 16.

Alternatively, you can use a different method. Since $10 \times 10 = 100$ and $20 \times 20 = 400$, the numbers are between 10 and 20 and since the product ends with 0, possibilities are 14×15 or 15×16 (10×11 is too low and 19×20 too high); 15×16 gives the correct answer.

(b) 21 and 22

(c) 43 and 44

Use guess and check, or the fact that since $40 \times 40 = 1600$ and $50 \times 50 = 2500$, the numbers are between 40 and 50. As the last digit is a 2, the possibilities for the consecutive integers are 41 and 42, 43 and 44, 46 and 47 or 48 and 49.

Use the calculator to check which give a product of 1892.

(d) 38 and 39

(e) 53 and 54

2 (a) 8, 9, 10 (b) 14, 15, 16

3 Yes; 59

4 (a) Test to see whether any of the prime numbers 2, 3, 5, 7 ..., up to the square root of the number, are factors. Students will not be aware of this method, but it can be explained to them. To find out whether 371 is prime, see if any of the numbers 2, 3, 5, 7, 11, 13, 17 or 19 are factors. As 7 is a factor ($7 \times 53 = 371$), 371 is not prime.

(b) 631 is prime. You need only test primes up to 25 for factors.

5 The numbers must be consecutive. Since $30 \times 30 = 900$ and $40 \times 40 = 1600$, the numbers are between 30 and 40. Now work out the units digit. Which consecutive numbers give a product ending in 2? They are 1 and 2, 3 and 4, 6 and 7 or 8 and 9. The tens digit must be 3, so use the calculator to check which will give a product of 1332: 36 and 37.

6 The answer will consist of the original number repeated: $273 \times 11 \times 91 = 273\,273$. This will always be so, since $11 \times 91 = 1001$, and to multiply any three-digit number by 1001 (11×91) will produce this result:
$abc \times 1001 = abc\ abc$.

7 (a) 3, 5, 8 (b) 5, 5, 6 (c) 7, 3, 6

8 The answer is always 37.

One reason is because $\dfrac{777}{21} = \dfrac{7 \times 111}{7 \times 3} = \dfrac{111}{3} = 37$

and this happens in each case.

Spirolaterals 1 (page 18)

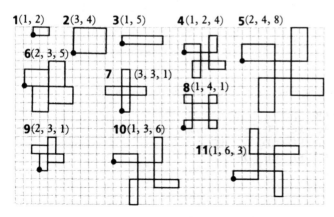

1(1, 2) **2**(3, 4) **3**(1, 5) **4**(1, 2, 4) **5**(2, 4, 8)
6(2, 3, 5)
7 (3, 3, 1)
8(1, 4, 1)
9(2, 3, 1) **10**(1, 3, 6)
11(1, 6, 3)

12(1, 2, 3, 3) **13**(1, 3, 3, 5) **14**(1, 5, 3, 3) **15**(2, 4, 6, 6)

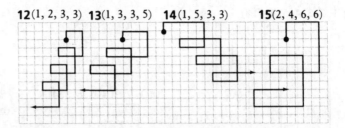

16(3, 1, 1, 1) **17**(1, 3, 1, 1) **18**(6, 2, 2, 2) **19**(5, 3, 1, 3) **20**(5, 3, 3, 1)

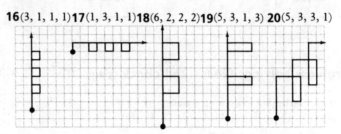

Descriptions of certain properties of these figures follow the solutions to Spirolaterals 2. Children should be encouraged to discuss properties, and all their findings.

Spirolaterals 2 (page 19)

1(1, 2, 3, 4, 5) **2**(1, 1, 2, 3, 3) **3**(2, 2, 3, 4, 4)

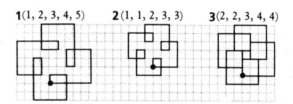

4 (2, 3, 3, 1, 1) **5**(1, 2, 3, 4, 5 ...) **6**(1, 1, 2, 2, 3, 3, 4, 4 ...)

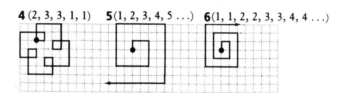

7(3, 4, 5, 6, 7 ...) **8**(2, 4, 6, 8, 10 ...) **9**(1, 2, 3, 4, 5, 6)

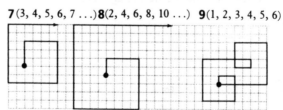

10(1, 1, 2, 2, 4, 4) **12**(1, 2, 3, 4, 5, 6, 7)
11(1, 1, 3, 4, 1, 2)

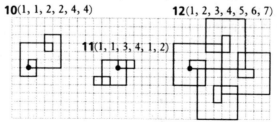

13 (1, 2, 3, 4, 5, 6, 7, 8)

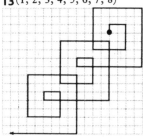

14 (1, 2, 3, 4, 5, 6, 3, 4)

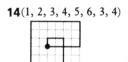

Problem solving: Guess and check (page 20)

1 It may be helpful to draw up a table.
   (a) 7, 5   (b) 8, 4   (c) 14, 1   (d) 32, 44   (e) 6, 18

2 (a) 8 (the numbers are 6, 7, 8)
   (b) 11 (the numbers are 7, 9, 11)

3 (a) 7 of each   (b) 8 of each

4

	Khalid	Joseph
(a)	£8	£7
(b)	£10	£5
(c)	£8.50	£6.50

5 £5 (binoculars cost £55)   **6** 10 and 5   **7** 20p (Karen had 10p)

In all these questions, drawing up a table and using guess-and-check strategy is one method that can be used.

Questions 4 and 5 can also be answered by acting out the problem in the following ways:

4 (a) Give Khalid £1, then share equally the remaining £14.
   (b) Give Khalid £5, then share equally the remaining £10.
   (c) Give Khalid £2, then share equally the remaining £13.

5 Allot £50 to the binoculars, then divide equally the remaining £10.

	Binoculars	Case
	£50	
	£ 5	£5
	£55	£5

Problem solving: Using tables (page 21)

The children can solve these using their own methods. They may, however, find tables helpful.

1 12 girls

Girls	Boys	Total
12	18	30

This question can also be answered by acting it out. Using two headings, 'Girls' and 'Boys', place 6 under 'Boys' and divide equally the remaining 24.

Girls	Boys
	6
12	12
12	18

2 10 boys

Girls	Boys	Total
20	10	30

3 (a) 11 questions

Answers		Total score
Correct (3 marks)	Incorrect (−1 mark)	
11	4	33 − 4 = 29

(b) 7 answers

Answers		Total score
Correct (5 marks)	Incorrect (−1 mark)	
23	7	115 − 7 = 108

4 Two 10p coins

50p	20p	10p	Total
4	14	2	£5

5 £9: This question can be answered using either guess and check or the fact that the family's tickets are equivalent to 7 children's or 3½ adult tickets, costing a total of £31.50. Therefore a child's ticket = £4.50 and an adult's ticket = £9.00.

6 36 years old
This question can be answered either by using guess and check (two numbers whose sum is 99, whose difference is 27 and whose digits are reversed) or by listing numbers whose digits are reversed and which differ by 27.

Julian's age	Dad's age
18	81
27	72
(36)	(63)
45	54

Problem solving: All the possibilities (page 22)

Children may need to be shown how to set out their work using tree diagrams.

1 (a) (i) 5 ways: A, B, C, D, E
       (ii) 20 ways

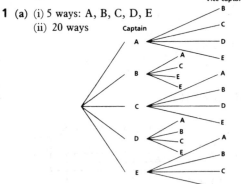

Reading along the branches, there are 20 possibilities:

AB	BA	CA	DA	EA
AC	BC	CB	DB	EB
AD	BD	CD	DC	EC
AE	BE	CE	DE	ED

(b) (i) 4 ways: A, B, D, E
(ii) 12 ways

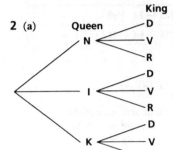

Reading along the branches, there are 12 possibilities:

AB BA DA EA
AD BD DB EB
AE BE DE ED

2 (a)

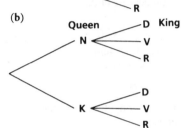

9 different pairs:

ND KD ID
NV KV IV
NR KR IR

(b)

6 different pairs:

ND
NV
NR
KD
KV
KR

(c)

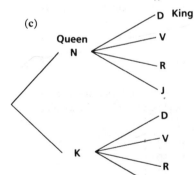

8 different pairs:

ND
NV
NR
NJ
KD
KV
KR
KJ

(d)

Students auditioning		Queen–King pairs
Girls	Boys	
1	2	2
2	2	4
2	3	6
3	2	6
3	3	9
3	4	12
4	3	12
4	4	16
4	5	20
5	5	25
5	6	30
6	6	36

Problem solving: Working backwards
(page 23)

1 (a) Start with 20. We are looking for the number that was doubled to give 20, so we need to halve it, giving 10. Now we are looking for the number to which 4 was added to give 10, so the original number was 6.

(b) Start with 16. Halve it (= 8), halve this (= 4) and halve again to give 2, the original number.

(c) Start with 6. Double it (= 12) and add 4 to give 16, the original number.

(d) Start with 6. Double it (= 12), add 3 (= 15) and divide this result by 5 to give 3, the original number.

(e) Start with 17. Subtract 8 (= 9). Now, since 9 is the square of 3, 3 was the number squared. Add 5 to give 8, the original number.

(f) Start with 2. Multiply by 5 (= 10), add 10 (= 20) and divide by 4 to give 5, the original number.

Note: In each of these solutions we used the inverse operation to work out the previous number. The inverse operation of:

addition is subtraction;
subtraction is addition;
multiplication is division;
division is multiplication;
doubling is halving;
halving is doubling.

Once children have their answers, they should check them by working through each problem from the beginning.

In 1(a) the answer was 6.

Checking this: start with 6, add 4, giving 10, double the result giving 20, which is the correct final answer.

2 Start with £2. Before the 50p coin was found, Anthony had £1.50. Before he bought the magazine he had £2.75 and before he spent the 75p he had £3.50. Therefore, his pocket money is £3.50.

3 Tahli must:
leave home at 8.20;
start breakfast at 8.05;
start dressing at 7.55;
get out of bed at 7.35.

4 Daniel had:
3 cards after game 4;
6 cards after game 3;
12 cards after game 2;
24 cards after game 1.
Therefore, he started with 48 cards.

Investigations with lines (page 24)

1 Some arrangements for four lines

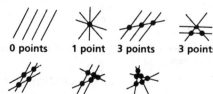

0 points   1 point   3 points   3 points

4 points   5 points   6 points

2 Some arrangements for five lines

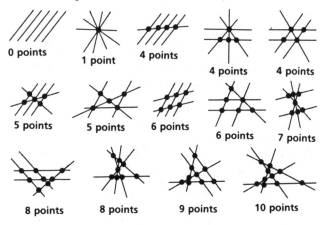

0 points
1 point
4 points
4 points
4 points
5 points
5 points
6 points
6 points
7 points
8 points
8 points
9 points
10 points

How many diagonals? (page 25)

Total diagonals

1

Sides	3	4	5	6	7	8	9	10
Vertices	3	4	5	6	7	8	9	10
Diagonals at each vertex	0	1	2	3	4	5	6	7
Total Diagonals	0	2	5	9	14	20	27	35

Possible patterns include:
- The number of vertices is the same as the number of sides.
- The number of diagonals at each vertex is three less than the number of sides (or of vertices).
- The difference between the numbers in the total number of diagonals is always increasing by one:

  Total diagonals   0   2   5   9   14   20   27   35

  Differences   2   3   4   5   6   7   8

- The total number of diagonals = the number of sides (or of vertices) × the number of diagonals at each vertex ÷ 2 (halved).

  Note that students are unlikely to discover this formula without some guidance.

2 From the above pattern, the number of diagonals for:
(a) a nonagon is 27; (b) a decagon is 36.

Cube explorations (page 26)

Children can build these solids to check their answers.

1 (a) 27 (This large cube is 3 × 3 × 3.)
  (b) 19 (children may become confused by the cubes with two or three faces showing.)
  (c) 8 (There are 27 cubes altogether of which 19 can be seen, so 8 cannot be seen.)

2 (a) 64 (This cube is 4 × 4 × 4.) (b) 37 (c) 27 (64 − 37)

3 Children can carry out experiments to solve these problems. To set up an experiment, use centicubes: start with a black cube, say, and around it construct a 3 × 3 × 3 solid of yellow cubes; around that build a 5 × 5 × 5 large red cube. Now remove in turn the cubes of each colour. If you start with a 2 × 2 × 2 cube and follow the same method, you will first build a 4 × 4 × 4 cube and then a 6 × 6 × 6 cube.

Size of cheese	Cubes cut	Cubes with wax	Cubes without wax
3 cm × 3 cm × 3 cm	27	27 − 1 = 26	1
4 cm × 4 cm × 4 cm	64	64 − 8 = 56	8
5 cm × 5 cm × 5 cm	125	125 − 27 = 98	27
6 cm × 6 cm × 6 cm	216	216 − 64 = 152	64

Mathematics is amazing (page 27)

1 In fact, all four-digit palindromic numbers are divisible by 11. We can prove this, by algebra; the proof is included here for teachers' interest (and for exceptionally bright children):
All four-digit palindromic numbers are of the form *abba* (e.g. 2992), which in fact is:

$$1000a + 100b + 10b + a = 1001a + 110b$$
$$= 11(91a + 10b)$$
$$= 11 \times \text{number}$$

Therefore, *abba* is divisible by 11.

2 (a) The answer will always be 22 for any three-digit number in which all digits are different.
  (b) If two of the digits are repeated, the answer will always be 11.

True or false? (page 28)

There are some very important mathematical concepts illustrated in these equations. Any ideas should be carefully discussed and problems clarified.

1	T	13	T	25	T	37	T	49	T
2	F	14	T	26	T	38	T	50	T
3	T	15	T	27	T	39	T	51	T
4	F	16	T	28	T	40	T	52	T
5	F	17	T	29	F	41	F	53	T
6	F	18	T	30	T	42	T	54	F
7	T	19	T	31	T	43	F	55	F
8	F	20	T	32	T	44	F	56	T
9	F	21	F	33	T	45	T	57	T
10	F	22	T	34	T	46	F	58	T
11	T	23	F	35	T	47	T	59	F
12	T	24	T	36	T	48	F	60	T

Repeating cycles (page 29)

1 (a)

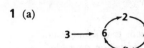

(b)

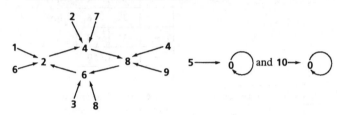

These can be summarised like this:

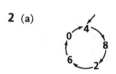

2 (a)

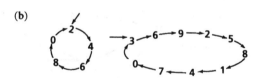

(b)

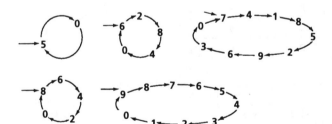

Area and perimeter investigations (page 30)

1 Rectangles with perimeter 16 m

Length (m)	Width (m)	Area (m²)
7	1	7
6	2	12
5	3	15
4	4	16

For a given perimeter, the square has the greatest area.

It is important to discuss with the children the fact that the square belongs to the family of rectangles, but the rectangle does not belong to the family of squares.

2 (a) Rectangles with perimeter 20 m

Width (m)	Length (m)	Area (m²)
1	9	9
2	8	16
3	7	21
4	6	24
5	5	25

Largest area: 25 m²

(b) Rectangles with perimeter 24 m

Width (m)	Length (m)	Area (m²)
1	11	11
2	10	20
3	9	27
4	8	32
5	7	35
6	6	36

Largest area: 36 m²

3 Rectangles with area 24 m²

Length (m)	Width (m)	Perimeter (m)
24	1	50
12	2	28
8	3	22
6	4	20

Shape with smallest perimeter:
6 m × 4 m

4 rectangles are possible.

(In fact, the smallest perimeter shape to give this area is the square, with a side of approximately 4.9 m.)

4 (a) Rectangles with area 36 m²

Length (m)	Width (m)	Perimeter (m)
36	1	74
18	2	40
12	3	30
9	4	26
6	6	24

Shape with smallest perimeter: 6 m × 6 m

(b) Rectangles with area 100 m²

Length (m)	Width (m)	Perimeter (m)
100	1	202
50	2	104
25	4	58
20	5	50
10	10	40

Shape with smallest perimeter: 10 m × 10 m

Finding areas (page 31)

1 Two possible methods are:

Method 1:
Length of AB = 16 m
Length of AH = 2 m
Area of ABIH = 32 m²
Area of DCJK = 32 m²
Length of QR = 8 m
Length of QI = 2 m
Area of QIJR = 16 m²
Area of HPSK = 16 m²
∴ Area of path = 96 m²

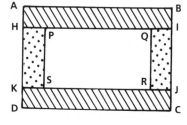

Method 2:
Length of AB = 16 m
Length of BC = 12 m
Area of ABCD = 192 m²
Area of PQRS = 96 m²
∴ Area of path = 192 m² − 96 m²
= 96 m²

2 (a) Area A + Area B = 20 × 6 + 13 × 5
= 120 + 65 = 185 m²
(b) Area C + Area D = 11 × 13 + 7 × 6
= 143 + 42 = 185 m²
(c) Area of large rectangle − area E = 11 × 20 − 7 × 5
= 220 − 35 = 185 m²

Area of triangles (page 32)

1 (a) 4 cm² (b) 6 cm² (c) 6 cm² (d) 9 cm²

2 (b) Area of triangle A = 5 cm²
Area of triangle B = 5 cm²
Area of triangle C = 10 cm²
Area of triangle D = 10 cm²
∴ First two statements are true

Shaded area (B + C) = 15 cm²
Shaded area (A + D) = 15 cm²
= shaded area (B + C)

Area of rectangle = 30 cm²
∴ Shaded area (B + C) = ½ area of rectangle

3 Area of shaded triangle = 12 cm² in each case
= ½ area of rectangle
= ½ base × perpendicular height
Therefore, if a triangle is inscribed within a rectangle so that its base is the length of the rectangle and its height is the width (or the other way around), the area of the triangle will be half the area of the rectangle.

4 Any triangle in which ½ base × perpendicular height = 12 cm² will be correct (that is, any triangle around which a rectangle drawn would have an area 24 cm²). These are some of the possible figures.

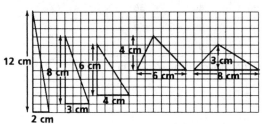

Problem solving: Organising lists 1 (page 33)

1

50p	20p	10p
2	–	–
1	2	1
1	1	3
1	–	5
–	5	–
–	4	2
–	3	4
–	2	6
–	1	8
–	–	10

2 The solutions to (b) (i), (ii) and (iii) are indicated on the table.

(a)

20p	10p	5p	(b)
2	1	–	
1	3	–	
1	2	2	(i)
1	1	4	
1	–	6	(ii)
–	5	–	(i)
–	4	2	
–	3	4	(ii)
–	2	6	(iii)
–	1	8	
–	–	10	

3

Captain	Vice-captain
A	B
A	C
A	D
B	A
B	C
B	D
C	A
C	B
C	D
D	A
D	B
D	C

or use a tree diagram and read along the branches:

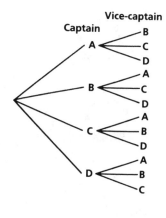

4

Bread	Filling
white	egg
white	cheese
white	tuna
white	honey
brown	egg
brown	cheese
brown	tuna
brown	honey

or use a tree diagram:

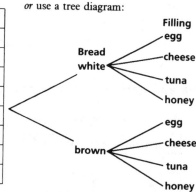

5 (a) 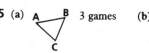 3 games (b) 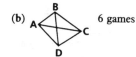 6 games

(c) 10 games

(d) A pattern is obvious from the above solutions: 3, 6 and 10 are the triangular numbers, so if 6 girls enter, 15 games will be played.

(e) 45 games will be played: $3 \to 6 \to 10 \to 15 \to 21 \to 28 \to 36 \to 45$

Problem solving: Organising lists 2 (page 34)

Children's attention should be drawn to the fact that there are several solutions to some of these questions.

1 (a)

Sets of 3	Sets of 4	Total number
1	3	15
5	–	15

(b) Children should be reminded to work systematically.

Sets of 3	Sets of 4	Sets of 5	Total number
–	2	3	23
1	–	4	23
1	5	–	23
2	3	1	23
3	1	2	23
5	2	–	23
6	–	1	23

2

3 kg packages at £4.20	5 kg packages at £6.50	Total cost
–	4	£26
1	3	£23.70
3	2	£25.60
*4	1	£23.30

* This is the best buy.

3

Number of cheques	Usual charge	New charge
25	£2.50	£1.50 + £1.25 = £2.75
30	£3.00	£1.50 + £1.50 = £3.00
40	£4.00	£1.50 + £2.00 = £3.50

To save money, you need to use more than 30 cheques each month.

4 (b): 1p + 2p + 4p + 8p + 16p + 32p + 64p = £1.27, which would be preferable.

5

Schools	A B C D E F G
Schedule of debates	B C D E F G
	C D E F G
	D E F G
	E F G
	F G
	G

∴ Total number = 6 + 5 + 4 + 3 + 2 + 1 = 21

 Alternatively, the information can be expressed in a diagram, and children can use this one as a model. There is a total of 21 lines.

Problem solving: Listing possibilities (page 35)

1 (a) At 9.10 p.m., since:
X will flash at 9.02, 9.04, 9.06, 9.08, 9.10
Y will flash at 9.05, 9.10
(or, since 2 and 5 are prime numbers and $2 \times 5 = 10$, they will flash together 10 minutes later).

(b) At 10.30 p.m., since:
X will flash at 10.06, 10.12, 10.18, 10.24, 10.30
Y will flash at 10.10, 10.20, 10.30
(or, since 6 and 10 are not prime, we in fact find the lowest common denominator, which is 30).

(c) (i) 11.15 p.m.   (iv) 11.44 p.m.   (vii) 11.15 p.m.
(ii) 11.21 p.m.   (v) 11.12 p.m.   (viii) 11.42 p.m.
(iii) 11.20 p.m.   (vi) 12.00 midnight   (ix) 11.30 p.m.

2 (a) 2, by rolling (1, 1)
(b) (i) (2, 6), (3, 5) (4, 4), (5, 3), (6, 2) 5 combinations
(ii) (6, 6) 1 combination.
(c) 7; (1, 6), (2, 5), (3, 4), (4, 3), (5, 2), (6, 1) 6 combinations

3 7 + 8 + 9 + 10 + 11 + 12 + 1 + 2 + 3 + 4 + 5 + 6 + 7 + 8 = 93 times

Area investigation 1 (page 36)

Graph paper and isometric graph paper are useful when considering the concept of area.

1

Original side (cm)	Original area (cm²)	Enlarged side (cm)	Enlarged area (cm²)
3	9	6	36
4	16	8	64
5	25	10	100
6	36	12	144
7	49	14	196

The enlarged area is four times the original area, so if you double the length of the sides of a square the new area is four times the original.

2

Original length and breadth (cm)		Original area (cm²)	Enlarged length and breadth (cm)		Enlarged area (cm²)
2	1	2	4	2	8
3	2	6	6	4	24
4	3	12	8	6	48
5	2	10	10	4	40

The new area is four times the original area.

3

	Original base and height (cm)		Original area (cm²)	Enlarged base and height (cm)		Enlarged area (cm²)
(a)	1	2	1	2	4	4
(b)	1	3	1½	2	6	6
(c)	2	3	3	4	6	12
(d)	1	1	½	2	2	2

The area of an enlarged triangle is four times the original area.

4 Irrespective of shape, if the length of a figure's sides is doubled the new area will be four times the area of the original shape.

Area investigations 2 (page 37)

Students should be provided with triangle grid paper.

1 For squares, rectangles or any other shape, if you treble the dimensions of the sides, the new enlarged area will be nine times the original area.

Consider the triangle: Consider the rhombus:

9 of the shaded shapes fit into large rhombus.

2 If the dimensions of a figure are multiplied by:

2	3	4	10

the new area will be 4   9   16   100 times as large as the original figure.